AGES 4-5
Reception

Gold Stars®

English

PaRragon

Bath · New York · Cologne · Melbourne · Delhi
Hong Kong · Shenzhen · Singapore · Amsterdam

Helping your child

⭐ Remember that the activities in this book should be enjoyed by your child. Try to find a quiet place to work.

⭐ Your child does not need to complete each page in one go. Always stop before your child grows tired, and come back to the same page another time.

⭐ It is important to work through the pages in the right order because the activities get progressively more difficult.

⭐ The answers to the activities are on page 32.

⭐ Always give your child lots of encouragement and praise.

⭐ Remember that the gold stars are a reward for effort as well as for achievement.

Written by Frances Mackay
Educational consultant: Dr Janet Rose
Illustrated by Simon Abbot and Adam Linley

First published by Parragon Books Ltd in 2015
Parragon Books Ltd
Chartist House
15-17 Trim Street
Bath BA1 1HA, UK
www.parragon.com

ISBN:978-1-4748-0183-6
Printed in China

Contents

Sounding out letters

Look at the pictures. Say the words. Sound out the beginning letters.

ant	a	aaa (not 'ay')
bat	b	b-b-b (not 'bee')
cat	c	ck (not 'see')
dog	d	duh (not 'dee')
egg	e	eh (not 'ee')
fish	f	fff (not 'eff')
goat	g	guh (not 'jee')
hat	h	hhh (not 'aitch')
igloo	i	ih (not 'eye')
jar	j	juh (not 'jay')
key	k	ck (not 'kay')
log	l	lll (not 'ell')

Note for parent: This activity helps your child to practise phonemes. Each letter is next to the sound it makes rather than its name.

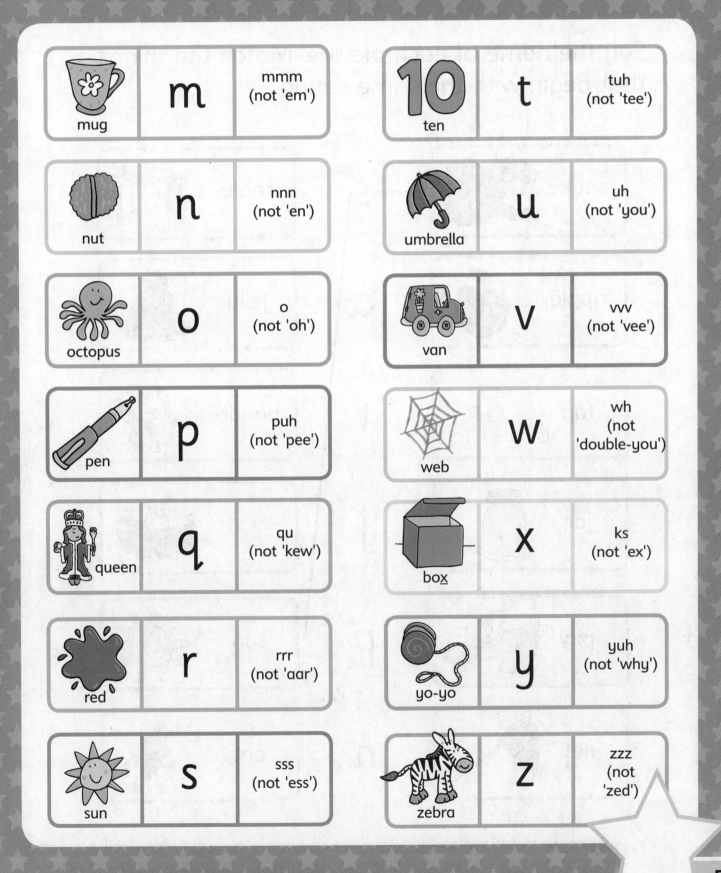

mug	m	mmm (not 'em')
ten	t	tuh (not 'tee')
nut	n	nnn (not 'en')
umbrella	u	uh (not 'you')
octopus	o	o (not 'oh')
van	v	vvv (not 'vee')
pen	p	puh (not 'pee')
web	w	wh (not 'double-you')
queen	q	qu (not 'kew')
box	x	ks (not 'ex')
red	r	rrr (not 'aar')
yo-yo	y	yuh (not 'why')
sun	s	sss (not 'ess')
zebra	z	zzz (not 'zed')

Beginning sounds

Say the name of each picture. Match the things that begin with the same sound.

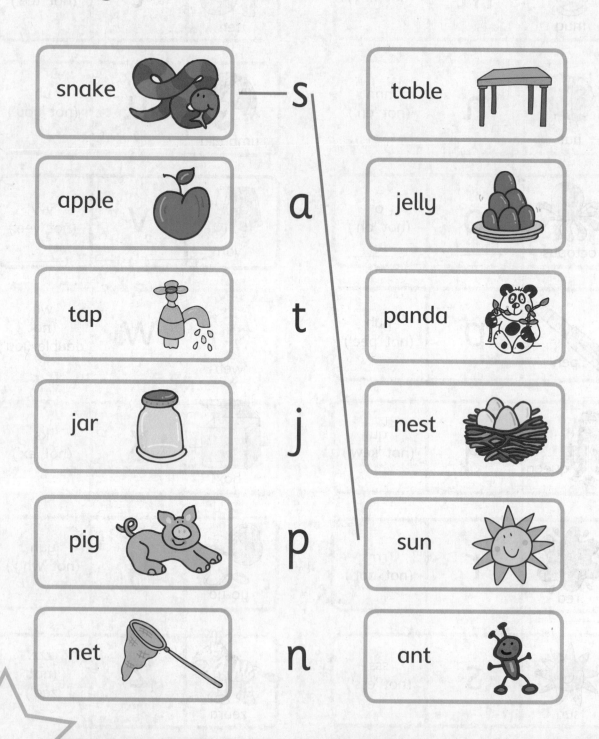

snake	s
apple	a
tap	t
jar	j
pig	p
net	n

table	
jelly	
panda	
nest	
sun	
ant	

cat	c	fox
elephant	e	monkey
hat	h	duck
fish	f	cup
rat	r	egg
moon	m	rabbit
dog	d	hand

More beginning sounds

Say the name of each picture. Circle the pictures in each row that have the same beginning sound.

 goat    duck    gate

 octopus   ostrich    van

 umbrella    upside-down    watch

 lion    arrow    lemon

 fish   duck   fox

Note for parent: This activity gives more practice in listening for and saying beginning sounds.

 juggler

 elephant

 jelly

 zebra

 zip

 teddy

 window

 lion

 witch

 violin

 van

 butterfly

 yo-yo

 apple

 yellow

 cow

 cap

rocket

Words that rhyme

Say the name of the picture on each card. Match the white cards with words that rhyme on coloured cards and then colour them the same.

mouse

car

bat

key

boat

frog

house

star

cat

tree

coat

dog

Note for parent: This activity helps your child hear end sounds that rhyme. Ask your child to say each word out loud. Can they think of other words that rhyme?

Match the rhymes

Say the name of the animal on each envelope.
Circle the picture that rhymes with it.

Make new words

Make new words by changing the beginning sounds. Use the letters in the box and the pictures to help you.

h f r c s m

tap	___ap
bun	___un
pen	___en
hat	___at
rug	___ug
van	___an

Find the sounds

Join each letter to the things in the picture that begin with the same sound.

| f | s | c | b |

Make up a story about what is happening in the picture.

Draw the words

Read the descriptions.
Draw the animals.

One day we went for a walk
and we saw...

...a big, buzzing,
busy bee,

... a spotty, slippery,
slithering snake,

...a pair of pretty,
pink pigs,

...and four funny,
floppy fish.

Note for parent: This activity practises beginning sounds word comprehension. Have fun describing
other animals your child might have seen.

Find the words

Find the words in the puzzle. Colour them in.

b	x	e	s	j	k
e	y	t	p	a	n
d	a	v	n	a	b
z	m	u	m	q	h
c	f	n	l	u	i
a	o	g	p	a	t
t	r	n	e	t	a
d	a	d	w	d	p

mum

dad

bed

pan

tap

cat

net

Write the words.

Note for parent: This activity gives your child practice in CVC words – consonant, vowel, consonant. Some words go across and some go down.

Sounds at the end

Say the name of each picture. Colour the letter that makes the sound at the end of the word.

Note for parent: This activity helps your child to listen for the final sound in a word. Encourage your child to think of other words that end in the same sounds.

More than one

Add an s sound at the end of a word when there is more than one thing.

 hat

 hats

Write the missing words.

1 car

2 _ _ _ _

1 bee

4 _ _ _ _

1 egg

2 _ _ _ _

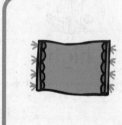

1 rug

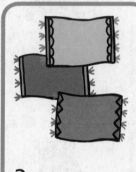

3 _ _ _ _

Opposites

Read the words in each row. Circle the word that has the opposite meaning to the first word.

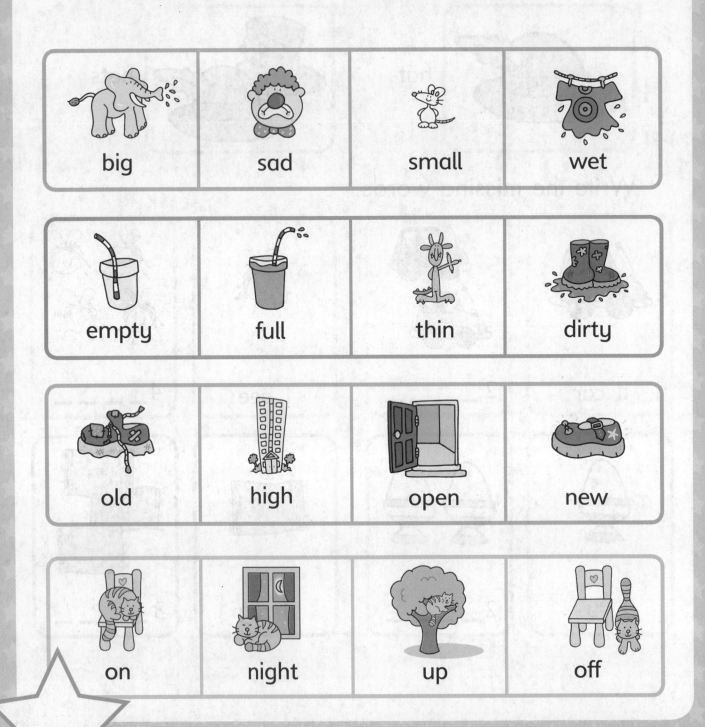

big	sad	small	wet
empty	full	thin	dirty
old	high	open	new
on	night	up	off

Note for parent: Learning opposites helps your child to understand their meanings.
Ask your child to guess the opposites to all the words on the page.

What happens next?

Draw what you think happens next.

Note for parent: This activity helps your child develop the idea of telling a simple story with a beginning, middle and ending.

19

ch and sh sounds

Say the word for each picture. Draw lines to join each picture to the correct beginning sound.

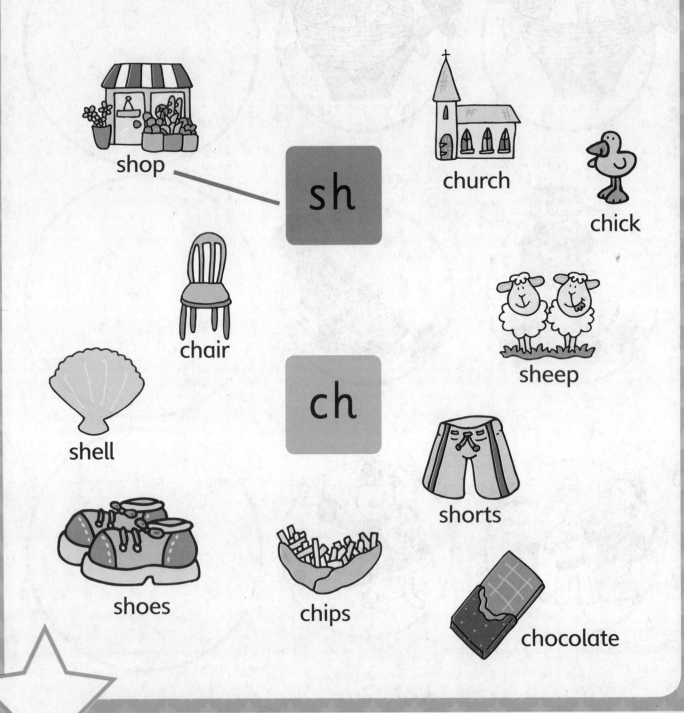

shop

sh

church

chick

chair

sheep

shell

ch

shorts

shoes

chips

chocolate

Note for parent: This activity helps your child learn that two letters can make one sound. It gives them practice in distinguishing between 'ch' and sh' sounds.

Use the pictures and words to complete the puzzle. All the words begin with the th sound.

thumb

thermometer

throne

thimble

thin

three

Note for parent: The **th** sound can be tricky to hear! Help your child to distinguish it from the *f* sound.

21

Middle sounds

Look at each picture and say the word. Circle the sound that is in the middle. Write the sound to finish the word.

	a i	p_n
	e u	b_s
	o e	l_g
	a e	w_b
	e a	c_t
	i e	n_t

Note for parent: It can be tricky to hear the sound in the middle. Help your child to read the words by sounding out each letter.

More middle sounds

Say the word in the basket.
Colour the balloons with the
same middle sound as the
word in the basket.

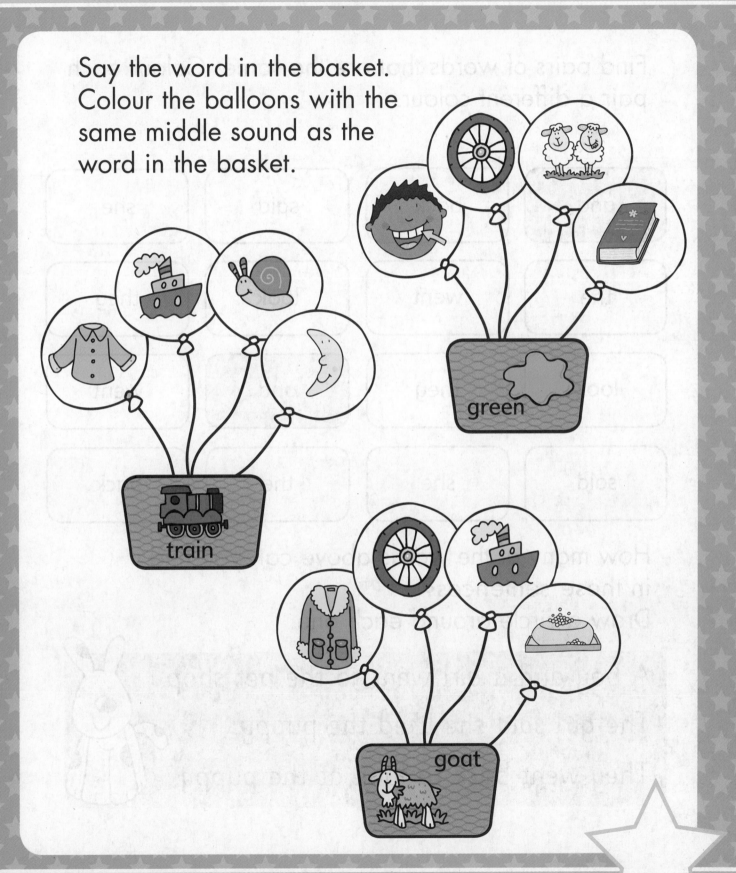

Note for parent: This activity gives your child more practice in recognising middle sounds and
understanding that two letters together can make one sound.

23

Colour the words

Find pairs of words that are the same. Colour each pair a different colour.

and	back	said	she
the	went	look	they
look	they	and	went
said	she	the	back

How many of the words above can you find
in these sentences?
Draw a circle around each one.

A boy and a girl went to the pet shop.

The girl said she liked the puppy.

They went back to look at the puppy.

Note for parent: This activity gives your child practice with common high frequency words. Explain that words at the start of a sentence begin with a capital letter.

Find the words

Find the little words in the big words. Circle the
little words.

the	mother
her	father
an	grandad
to	octopus
in	window
on	crayon

Sentences

Use the pictures and words to complete the sentences.

coat   door   desk   chair

dinosaur

bed

net

The coat is on the back of the d _ _ _.
The n _ _ is under the bed.
The d _ _ _ _ _ _ _ is on the bed.
The chair is near the d _ _ _.

Capital letters

Look at these names. They all begin with a capital letter.

> Jack   Emma   Oliver   Lily

Draw lines to match the capital letters to the small letters.

> B   G   D   A   E   F   M

> f   e   b   m   d   g   a

Colour all the capital letters in the puzzle.

A	x	E	s	J	C
b	H	q	F	w	k
L	a	B	z	I	K
D	r	e	G	t	u

Note for parent: Tell your child that names always begin with a capital letter. Together, write out the names of people in your family.

27

Tell the story

Trace the fishing lines to see what each person has caught.

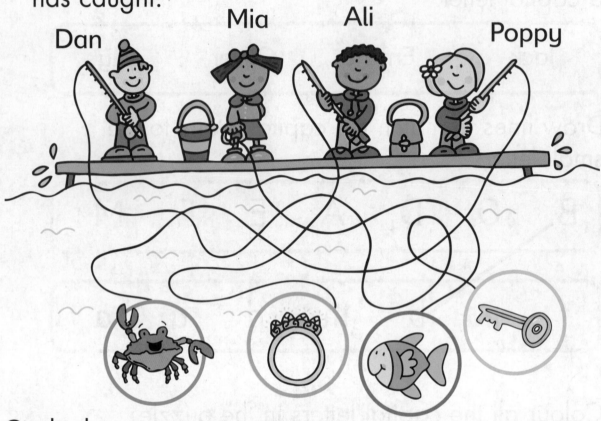

Dan Mia Ali Poppy

Circle the correct answer.

Who caught the fish?	Dan	Poppy	Mia
Who caught the crab?	Poppy	Dan	Ali
What did Dan catch?	key	crab	ring
What would you like to catch?	ring	fish	crab

Now make up a story about the children.

Note for parent: This activity encourages your child to look carefully. Read the questions to your child.

Odd one out

Say the words in each group. Listen to the sounds.
Circle the odd one out in each group.

Note for parent: Say the words with your child and listen carefully to the different sounds. The sounds that are the same may come at the beginning, middle or end of the word.

29

Make a story

Look at the four pictures to see what is happening. Write the numbers 1 to 4 in the boxes to show their correct order.

Draw or write what you think happens next.

Note for parent: This activity gives your child practice in story sequencing. Talk about what is happening in each picture. Work out the order of the story.

Tricky words

Look at the shapes of these words. Write the words in the matching boxes.

little they what some like
when said have was all do

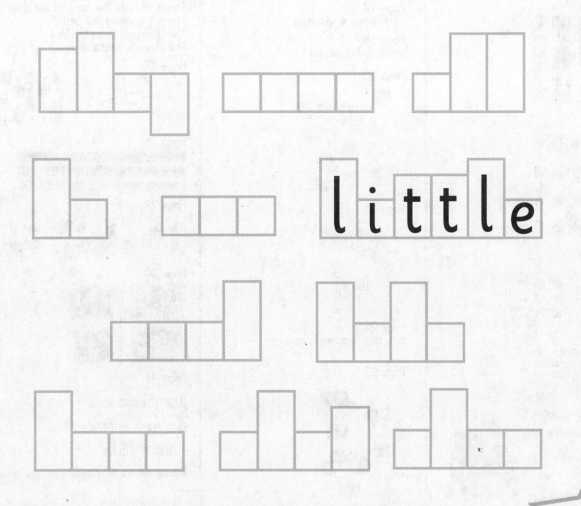

Note for parent: This activity gives your child practice in learning some tricky high frequency words.
The shape of a word can help your child to recognize it when reading.

31

Answers

Page 6

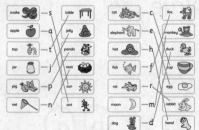

Page 8

Page 10

Page 11

Page 12

Page 13

Or: slide, snail, cloud, butterfly, boy

Page 15

Page 16

Page 17

cars, bees, eggs, rugs

Page 18

small, full, new, off

Page 20

Page 21

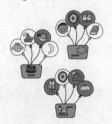

Page 22

pin, bus, log, web, cat, net

Page 23

Page 24

A boy and a girl went to the pet shop. The girl said she likes the puppy. They went back to look at the puppy.

Page 25

mother
father
grandad
octopus
window
crayon

Page 26

The coat is on the back of the door.
The net is under the bed.
The dinosaur is on the bed.
The chair is near the desk.

Page 27

Page 28

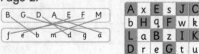

Page 29

Page 30

2, 4, 1, 3

Page 31

they some all
do was little
said like
have what when